Packed full of dino fun...

NATURAL HISTORY MUSEUM

THE WORLD OF DINOSAURS 2020 EDITION

THIS BOOK BELONGS TO

_____

Write your name here.

Written by Catherine Such

Published 2019.

Little Brother Books, Ground Floor,
23 Southernhay East, Exeter, Devon, EX1 1QL

Printed In Poland.

books@littlebrotherbooks.co.uk | www.littlebrotherbooks.co.uk

The Little Brother Books trademark, email and website
addresses, are the sole and exclusive properties of
Little Brother Books Limited.

Turn the page to begin your dinosaur adventure...

Mighty Tyrannosaurus

Meet the dino king!

WOW!

Tyrannosaurus lived in Canada and the USA 67-65 million years ago.

DINO REPORT

NAME: Tyrannosaurus
(tye-RAN-oh-sore-us)

MEANING: Tyrant lizard

SIZE:

FOOD: Meat

It walked on two legs.

DID YOU KNOW?

A Tyrannosaurus's mighty bite was three times as powerful as a lion's.

Sharp sense of smell to sniff out prey.

DID YOU KNOW?

Tyrannosaurus had a huge brain, twice the size of other giant meat-eaters.

60 long, sharp teeth.

Tiny arms compared to rest of body.

FOSSIL FINDS

These fantastic dinosaur fossils have been discovered. Can you circle the one that belongs to a Tyrannosaurus?

A

B

C

Answers on pages 76-77.

Which Way?

This slow-moving Stegosaurus has lost its way. Can you guide it back to its home at the foot of the volcano, avoiding the rocks along the way?

START

How many of each of these things does the Stegosaurus pass on its way home?

Answers on pages 76-77.

Big Brachiosaurus

This tall dino could feast on leaves from the tallest trees.

WOW!

Brachiosaurus lived in Algeria, Portugal, Tanzania and the USA 155-140 million years ago.

DID YOU KNOW?

The Brachiosaurus could use its long tail to rest on when reaching up to tall trees – like having an extra leg.

DINNERTIME!

How many leaves can you count in this leafy jumble?

Held its head high.

DID YOU KNOW?

The Brachiosaurus spent weeks digesting its food in its powerful gut to get all the nutrients out of it.

Pencil-shaped teeth.

Really long neck.

DINO REPORT

NAME: Brachiosaurus
(BRAK-ee-oh-sore-us)

MEANING: Arm lizard

SIZE:

FOOD: Plants

Long front legs.

Answers on pages 76-77.

Dino Finds

Discover where in the world dinosaur fossils have been found.

Triceratops

NORTH AMERICA

Stegosaurus

Ankylosaurus

Tyrannosaurus

SOUTH AMERICA

Trace over the words to discover which country had the most kinds of dinosaurs.

The USA

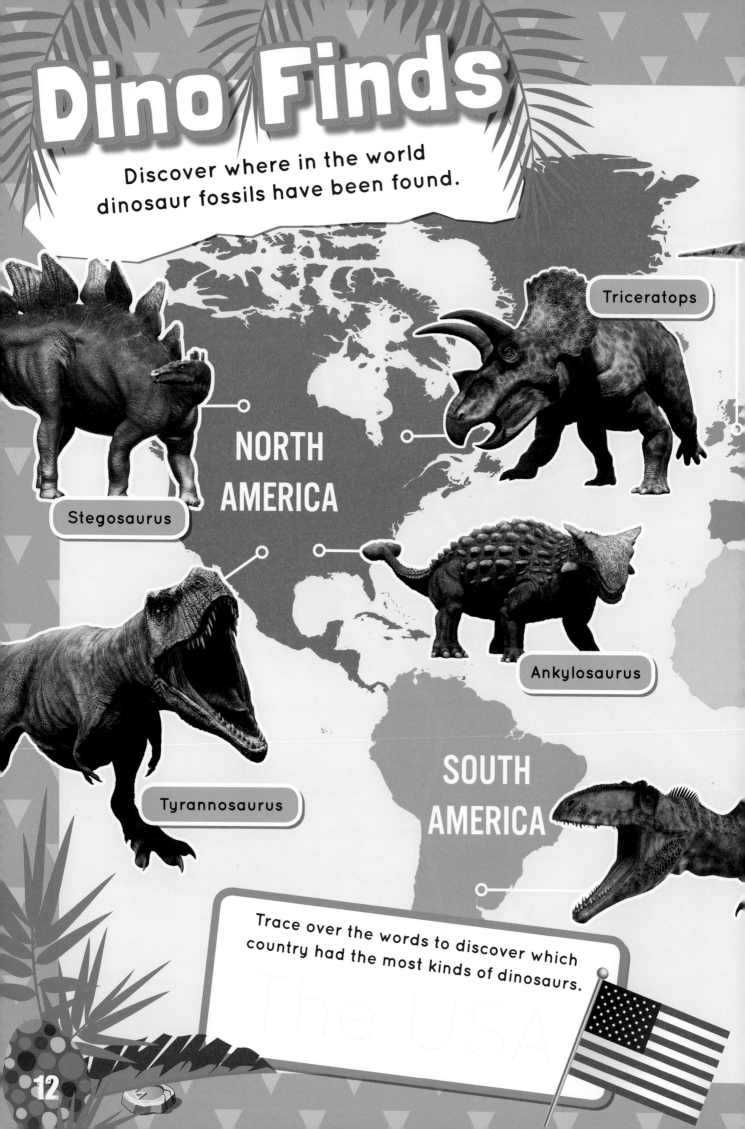

Toothless Oviraptor

Find out more about this desert dinosaur.

WOW!

Oviraptor lived in Mongolia 85-75 million years ago.

DINO REPORT

NAME: Oviraptor
(OH-vee-RAP-tor)

MEANING: Egg thief

SIZE:

FOOD: Meat — Plants

Walked on two legs.

DID YOU KNOW?

Oviraptors couldn't chew flesh as they had no teeth so they may have swallowed reptiles or crunched on fruit and nuts instead.

Beak-like mouth.

No teeth.

Curved jaws to crush hard objects.

DID YOU KNOW?

The Oviraptor was mistakenly thought to steal eggs from the nests of other dinosaurs which is how it got the name 'egg thief'.

COUNT THE EGGS

How many eggs has the Oviraptor laid in its nest?

Answers on pages 76-77.

Dotty Dino

Join the dots to finish this picture of a Diplodocus, then colour the dino in.

SPOT IT!

Can you find this flying reptile?

Colour the footprints when you've finished.

16

Jurassic Jokes!

Make your friends laugh with these roar-some dinosaur jokes!

What do you call a dinosaur with no eyes?
Do-you-think-he-saurus!

FUNNY RATING

What makes more noise than a dinosaur?
Two dinosaurs!

FUNNY RATING

What does a Triceratops sit on?
It's Tricera-bottom!

FUNNY RATING

What's as big as a dinosaur but weighs nothing?
A dinosaur's shadow!

FUNNY RATING

What has three horns and four wheels?
A Triceratops on a skateboard!

FUNNY RATING

What do you call a sleeping dinosaur?
A dino-snore!

FUNNY RATING

LAUGH-O-METER!
1 2 3 4 5

Give each joke a funny rating out of 5.

Terrific Triceratops

The last horned dinosaur to walk the Earth.

DINO REPORT

NAME: Triceratops
(tri-SERRA-tops)

MEANING:
Three-horned face

SIZE:

FOOD: Plants

Horns for fighting or fending off attackers.

Sharp beak used to nip low growing plants.

800 tiny teeth.

Large frill to protect its neck.

DID YOU KNOW?

The bulky Triceratops was too heavy to walk quickly.

ODD ONE OUT

One of these Triceratops pictures is different from the rest. Can you circle the odd one out?

A

B

C

DID YOU KNOW?

The Triceratops was the largest of the horned dinosaurs.

WOW!

Triceratops lived in the USA 68-66 million years ago.

Answers on pages 76-77.

Speedy Coelophysis

Introducing the fast and fierce lizard-eater.

WOW!

Coelophysis lived in South Africa, the USA and Zimbabwe 225-220 million years ago.

Long tail for balancing when running fast.

DINO REPORT

NAME: Coelophysis (seel-OH-fie-sis)

MEANING: Hollow form

SIZE:

FOOD: Meat

RUNAWAY DINO

Trace over the trail this fast Coelophysis has made.

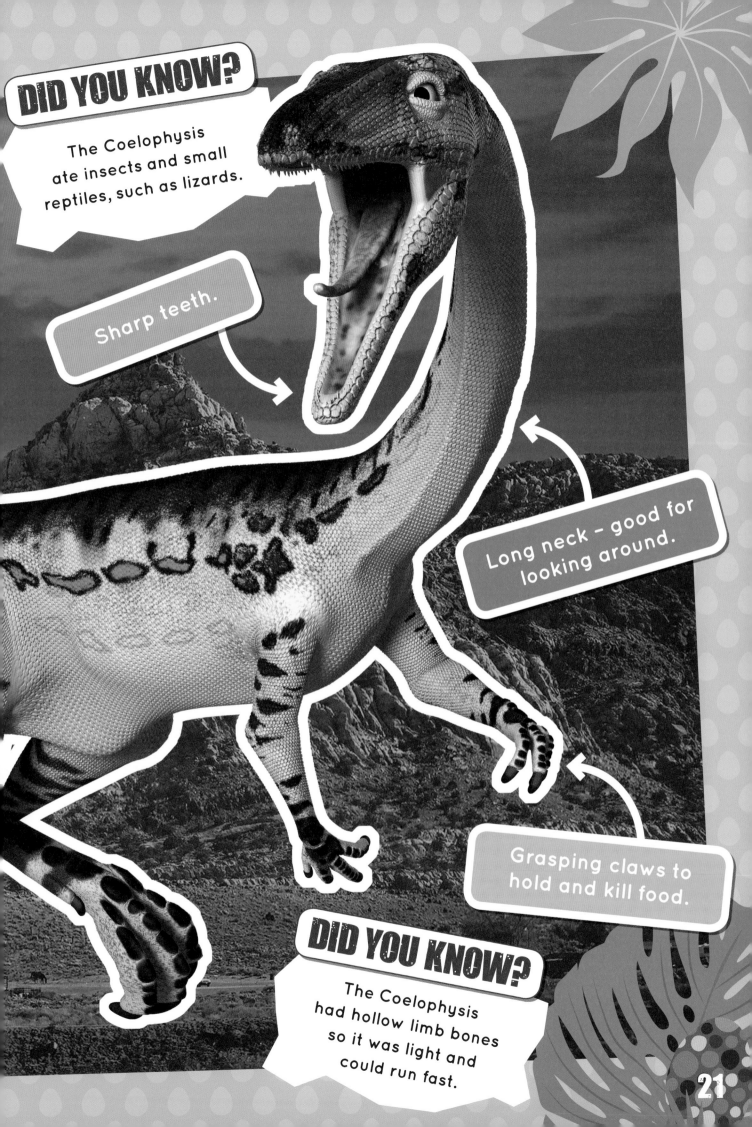

DID YOU KNOW?

The Coelophysis ate insects and small reptiles, such as lizards.

Sharp teeth.

Long neck – good for looking around.

Grasping claws to hold and kill food.

DID YOU KNOW?

The Coelophysis had hollow limb bones so it was light and could run fast.

21

Dinosaur Differences

Time yourself to see how quickly you can spot the eight differences between these two prehistoric pictures.

Colour a dinosaur footprint each time you spot a change.

HOW LONG DID IT TAKE?

Less than a minute = colour the clock red.
1-3 minutes = **colour the clock blue.**
More than 3 minutes = colour the clock green.

Answers on pages 76-77.

Super Spinosaurus

Meet the longest meat-eating dinosaur.

WOW!

Spinosaurus lived in Egypt and Morocco 95-70 million years ago.

DID YOU KNOW?

Spinosaurus hunted on land and in shallow water.

DINO REPORT

NAME: Spinosaurus (SPINE-oh-SORE-us)

MEANING: Thorn lizard

SIZE:

FOOD: Meat   Fish

Webbed toes for walking in water.

DID YOU KNOW?

A Spinosaurus's jaws were long and narrow, like a crocodile's.

High up nostrils for breathing in water.

Enormous sail.

Long jaw and sharp teeth.

SPOT THE BIGGEST

Look closely at these pictures of a roaring Spinosaurus. Can you circle the biggest?

 **A**

 **B**

 **C**

Answers on pages 76-77.

Funny Feet!

Stomp like a dinosaur with these easy-to-make dino feet.

YOU WILL NEED:

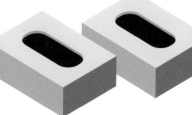

Two empty rectangular tissue boxes

A4 piece of thin orange card

Green paint

Paintbrush

Scissors   Glue

HOW TO MAKE

1

Ask an adult to cut holes in the tissues boxes, big enough for your feet to fit inside.

2

Paint the tissue boxes green and leave to dry.

3 Cut some spikes out of orange card and glue them to the front of the tissue boxes.

4 Once the glue has dried, your dino feet are ready to wear.

Where will you stomp in your dino feet?

COUNT IT! How many baby dinos are hidden on these pages?

Answers on pages 76-77.

Bulky Iguanodon

This heavy dinosaur had an unusual weapon.

WOW!

Iguanodon lived in Belgium, England and the USA 140-110 million years ago.

DINO REPORT

NAME: Iguanodon
(ig-WHA-noh-don)

MEANING: Iguana tooth

SIZE:

FOOD: Plants

Could walk on four or two legs.

QUESTION TIME

How many digits did an Iguanodon have on each hand? Copy the letters below into the matching coloured circles to find out.

◯ ◯ ◯ ◯

I V E F

DID YOU KNOW?

When Iguanodon was first discovered, scientists thought its thumb spike was a horn on its head.

Curved and grooved teeth – good for grinding.

Long tongue.

DID YOU KNOW?

Iguanodon was the first ever dinosaur to be identified, after miners in Sussex, England, dug up some Iguanodon teeth 200 years ago.

Large thumb spike to fend off predators.

Answers on pages 76-77.

Shadow Fun

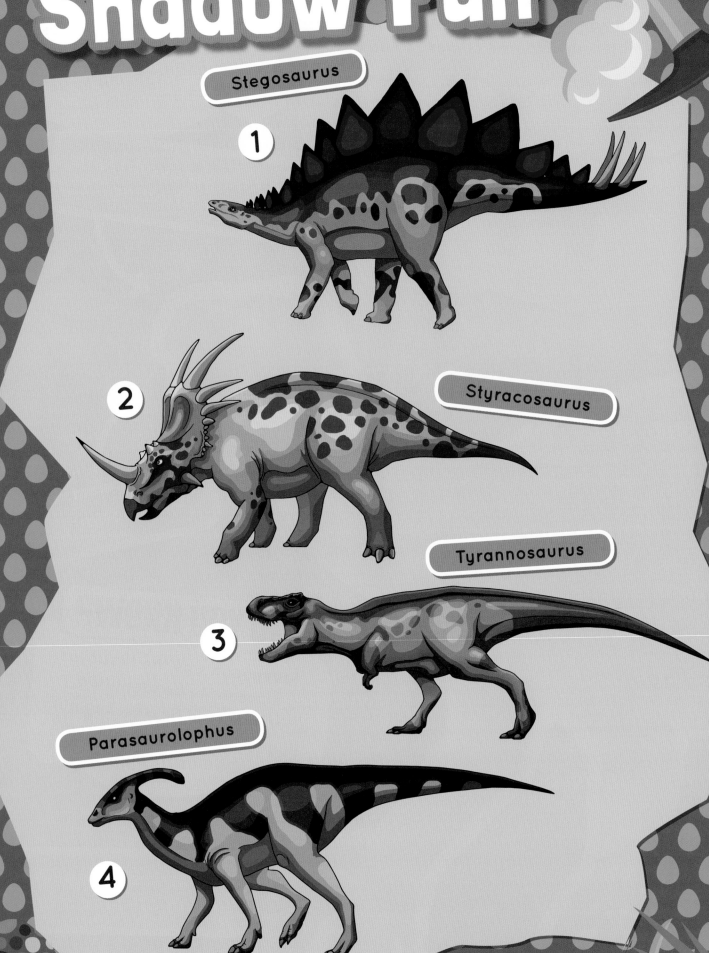

Stegosaurus

1

2

Styracosaurus

Tyrannosaurus

3

Parasaurolophus

4

Dino alert! Can you match these prehistoric predators to their shadows?

A

B

C

D

Colour the dino egg when you've finished.

Answers on pages 76-77.

Slow Stegosaurus

Introducing one of the largest of the plate-backed plant-eaters.

Spiked tail to defend against predators.

WOW!

Stegosaurus lived in the USA 156-144 million years ago.

DELICIOUS DINNER

Draw a plate of yummy food for this plant-eating Stegosaurus.

A Stegosaurus's back plates may have flashed red to scare off attackers.

Two rows of bony back plates.

DINO REPORT

NAME: Stegosaurus
(STEG-oh-SORE-us)

MEANING: Roof lizard

SIZE:

FOOD: Plants

Tiny brain, the size of a walnut.

Sharp beak used to nip low growing plants.

DID YOU KNOW?

Stegosaurus tail fossils show lots of damage which might have been caused by fighting.

My Favourite Dinosaur

Draw a picture of your dinosaur here.

Are you crazy about the mighty Tyrannosaurus? Or does the ginormous Diplodocus rock your world? Make this page all about your fave dino.

My favourite dinosaur is ....

The most awesome thing about it is..

The words that best describe my dinosaur are:

☐ Big

☐ Small

☐ Plant-eater

☐ Meat-eater

☐ Fast

☐ Fierce

☐ Scary

☐ Powerful

Here's a cool fact about my fave dino:..

....

Word Hunt

Can you find these dinosaur words hidden in the wordsearch below?

Answers on pages 76-77.

SPOT IT!

Can you find this dinosaur nest?

Colour a footprint as you find each word.

FOOTPRINT

FOSSIL

EGG

HORN

PREDATOR

BONES

NEST

PREHISTORIC

F	O	O	T	P	R	I	N	T	A	P
Y	S	T	E	O	T	F	I	J	O	R
A	F	R	T	H	O	R	N	T	U	E
K	O	L	S	A	R	E	D	E	I	H
M	S	F	Z	N	O	K	E	G	S	I
C	S	F	S	E	Y	W	V	G	I	S
T	I	U	I	S	K	G	G	D	S	T
N	L	C	A	T	A	O	J	E	S	O
B	G	R	P	R	E	D	A	T	O	R
S	A	C	E	V	X	S	P	R	J	I
B	O	N	E	S	D	O	V	H	H	C

35

Giant Giganotosaurus

Find out more about one of the world's largest dinos.

WOW!

Giganotosaurus lived in Argentina 112-90 million years ago.

Solid, bulky body.

DINO REPORT

NAME: Giganotosaurus
(gig-an-OH-toe-SORE-us)

MEANING:
Giant southern lizard

SIZE:

FOOD: Meat

DID YOU KNOW?
Giganotosaurus had a small brain for such a huge dinosaur – it was about the size of a cucumber.

DINO CLOSE-UPS

Which of these close-ups doesn't belong to the Giganotosaurus?

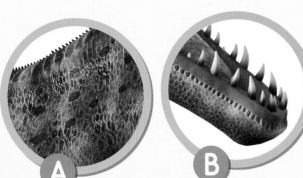

A

B

C

D

Good sense of smell.

Long, blade-like teeth – good for slicing.

Short arms with three fingers on each hand.

DID YOU KNOW?

The only evidence scientists have of Giganotosaurus is one skeleton and a piece of jawbone.

Answers on pages 76-77.

Dino Dice Game

Get ready to roar and stomp like a dinosaur with this fun action game.

YOU WILL NEED:

Scissors   Glue

HOW TO MAKE

1. Ask an adult to cut out the dice opposite or photocopy the page.

2. Fold the dice along the dotted lines to make a cube shape.

3. Add glue to the seven flaps and stick your dice together.

HOW TO PLAY

1. Make your dice following the instructions above.

2. Take it in turns to roll the dice and do whichever dinosaur action it lands on.

3. Keep playing for as long as you like.

Adult guidance is needed for this activity.

Make sure you read page 40 before you cut your dice out.

ROAR

Like a Tyrannosaurus

Glue here

Glue here

FLAP

Glue here

Like a Microraptor

STOMP

Like a Triceratops

Glue here

SWING

Like a Ankylosaurus

Glue here

Glue here

STRETCH

Like a Diplodocus

Glue here

CHOMP

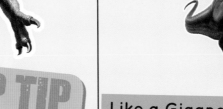

Like a Giganotosaurus

Glue here

TOP TIP

You can also play this game on your own.

39

Almighty Apatosaurus

This gigantic dino roamed across the USA.

WOW!

Apatosaurus lived in the USA 154-145 million years ago.

Apatosaurus swallowed stones to help grind up its food in its stomach.

Long tail used for balance.

DINO REPORT

NAME: Apatosaurus
(ah-PAT-oh-sore-us)

MEANING:
Deceptive lizard

SIZE:

FOOD: Plants

Walked on four legs.

Spoon-shaped teeth inside.

DID YOU KNOW?

The Apatosaurus could crack its tail like a whip, making a sound louder than a cannon.

DINO COLOURING

Colour this Apatosaurus to make it blend in with the plants.

DID YOU KNOW?

The Apatosaurus laid eggs the size of basketballs.

41

Spotted!

Become a prehistoric explorer with this awesome search and find puzzle.

Tick a circle as you spot each one.

Answers on pages 76-77.

43

Giant Diplodocus

This huge creature was one of the largest dinosaurs.

WOW!

Diplodocus lived in the USA 155-145 million years ago.

Long tail with 80 backbones.

DINO REPORT

NAME: Diplodocus (DIP-low DOCK-us)

MEANING: Double beam

SIZE:

FOOD: Plants

Powerful back legs, longer than the front legs.

SUPER SEQUENCE

What colour Diplodocus footprint comes next in the sequence below? Colour the last footprint the correct colour.

Answers on pages 76-77.

DID YOU KNOW?

The enormous Diplodocus was as long as a blue whale.

Long neck to reach high and low plants.

Stones in the stomach helped digest food.

DID YOU KNOW?

A Diplodocus's tail made a booming sound when whipped which might have scared off predators.

Fantastic Fossils

Finding fossils is tricky but making them is easy! Follow this super simple recipe to create fossils of your favourite dinos.

YOU WILL NEED:

125g plain flour   150g salt

120ml water

Small plastic dinosaurs

Adult guidance is needed for this activity.

HOW TO MAKE

1 Sift the flour into a bowl then mix in the salt.

2 Add the water, a spoonful at a time, mixing continuously until the mixture forms a dough.

SPOT IT!

Find the Triceratops fossil hidden on these pages.

3

On a floured surface, form the dough into flattened rock shapes then press a plastic dinosaur into the dough to leave an imprint. Carefully remove the toy.

4

TOP TIP

Ask a grown up to hide your dinosaur fossils for you to find.

Line a baking tray with greaseproof paper and cook your fossils on the lowest heat for three hours or until they're hard.

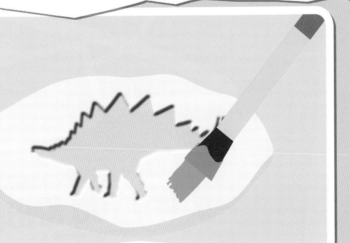

Colour the dinosaur when you've finished.

5

Leave to cool before removing from the tray. If you want, you can then paint your fossils.

Mini Microraptor

This tiny dino was about the size of a seagull.

WOW!

Microraptor lived in China 125-122 million years ago.

Sharp claws.

DINO REPORT

NAME: Microraptor
(MIKE-row-rap-tor)

MEANING: Tiny plunderer

SIZE:

FOOD: Meat

DID YOU KNOW?

Microraptor had a fan of feathers at the end of its tail which may have helped it to balance in the air.

DID YOU KNOW?

Microraptor was able to use its wings to glide but couldn't fly like a bird.

Small, sharp, pointed teeth.

Bird-like wings.

Covered in feathers.

SPOT THE SMALLEST

Can you circle the smallest Microraptor?

A

B

C

D

E

Answers on pages 76-77.

49

Handprint Picture

Make sure you rea[d] page 52 before yo[u] cut your dinosaur picture out.

Use your handprints to make a fun dino picture then name the dinosaur after yourself!

YOU WILL NEED:

Scissors

Paint

Paintbrush

Adult guidance is needed for this activity.

HOW TO MAKE

1. Ask an adult to cut out the picture of the dinosaur on the opposite page.

2. Write your name at the top to name your dinosaur. For example, if your name is Sam, your dinosaur would be called Samosaurus.

3. Use a paintbrush to cover one of your hands in paint then make a handprint on the dinosaur's back.

4. Keep adding handprints along the length of the dinosaur's back and tail.

5. Leave to dry then hang your picture up for everyone to see.

SAM osaurus
(Write your name here)

50

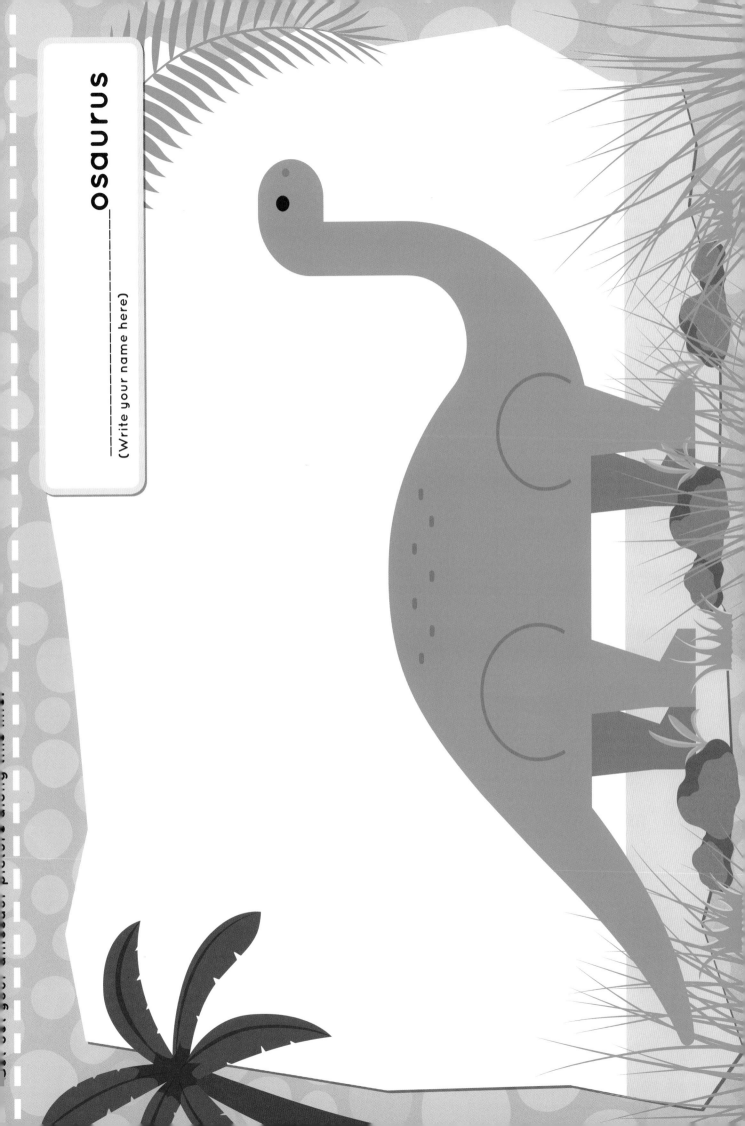

osaurus

_____
(Write your name here)

Fierce Allosaurus

Meet the North American king of Jurassic predators.

WOW!

Allosaurus lived in Portugal and the USA 156-144 million years ago.

DINO REPORT

NAME: Allosaurus (AL-oh-saw-russ)

MEANING: Other lizard

SIZE:

FOOD:  Meat

DID YOU KNOW?

Allosaurus teeth curved backwards to stop prey escaping.

Feet with three toes.

70 dagger-like teeth.

Powerful jaws.

Hands with three strong claws.

DID YOU KNOW?

An almost complete Allosaurus fossil was discovered in the USA in 1991. It was nicknamed 'Big Al'.

HEADING HOME

Which path should this Allosaurus take to get back home?

A

B

C

Answers on pages 76-77.

Twilight Trail

Draw a path to guide this Ankylosaurus back to its nest before it gets dark.

START

Count the bones.

Colour these leaves for the Ankylosaurus to eat.

54

Dodge the flying reptiles.

Avoid the Allosaurus!

Colour 4 eggs blue and 3 eggs green.

FINISH

Musical Parasaurolophus

This duckbill dino could make music!

WOW!

Parasaurolophus lived in Canada and the USA 76-74 million years ago.

Unusual shaped tail.

Could stand on back legs to reach food high up.

DINO REPORT

NAME: Parasaurolophus
(pa-ra-saw-ROL-off-us)

MEANING:
Like ridged lizard

SIZE:

FOOD: Plants

DID YOU KNOW?

Parasaurolophus may have used the sound from its crest to talk to other dinosaurs.

DID YOU KNOW?

A paleontologist worked out the sound a Parasaurolophus's crest would have made by making a crest out of a tube and blowing into it.

Fancy crest that made a sound like a trumpet.

Wide, flat mouth like a duck's beak.

DINO DRAWING

Trace over the lines to draw this Parasaurolophus then colour it in.

Make a Mask

Make and wear this terrific Triceratops mask. You'll look roar-some!

YOU WILL NEED:

Paper plate

A4 piece of thin card   Paper straw

Paint   Sticky tape

Paintbrushes

Scissors   Glue

HOW TO MAKE

1

Ask an adult to cut a paper plate in half and then cut a wavy pattern around the edge of the plate and cut out two eye holes.

2

Paint the plate green and paint the card yellow. Leave to dry.

3

Cut out four triangular shapes from the yellow card.

4

Glue the yellow triangles onto your mask to make the dinosaur's horns and nose.

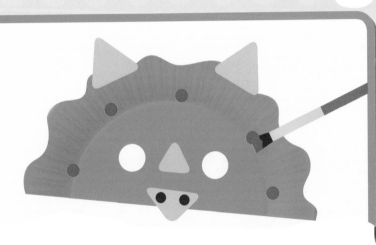

5

Use red paint to add spots to your dinosaur and blue paint to add nostrils to its nose.

6

When all the paint is dry, use sticky tape to attach a paper straw to your mask so you can hold it in front of your face.

Follow the footprints to the Triceratops then colour it in.

Adult guidance is needed for this activity.

Fast Velociraptor

This poodle-sized dino was small but speedy.

Velociraptor lived in Mongolia 74-70 million years ago.

DINO REPORT

NAME: Velociraptor
(vel-OSS-ee-rap-tor)

MEANING:
Quick plunderer

SIZE:

FOOD: Meat

Long stiff tail for balance.

DID YOU KNOW?

Velociraptor hunted in packs and probably ate small lizards, mammals, baby dinosaurs and eggs.

Large eyes to look for prey.

DID YOU KNOW?

Velociraptor was smart for a dinosaur and had a large brain for its size.

Jagged teeth.

Large hooked claws.

EGG MATCH

Can you draw lines to join these broken eggs back together?

Answers on pages 76-77.

61

Colouring Game

YOU WILL NEED:

A dice

Two pens

Play this fun game with a friend. The first one to colour their Stegosaurus is the winner.

PLAYER 1

62

HOW TO PLAY

1. Decide who will be player 1 and who will be player 2.

2. Take it in turns to roll a dice – each number corresponds to a part of your dinosaur's body.

3. Check the key then colour the corresponding part of your dinosaur.

4. Keep playing until one player has coloured all of their dinosaur – that player is the winner.

SPOT IT!

Can you find 10 dinosaur footprints?

Key
1 = Head
2 = Body
3 = Tail
4 = Front legs
5 = Back legs
6 = Plates

PLAYER 2

Quick Dilophosaurus

This fast runner had an unusual double crest on its head.

WOW!

Dilophosaurus lived in the USA 190 million years ago.

DID YOU KNOW?

Dilophosaurus probably fought other dinosaurs a lot.

GRUB'S UP!

Draw a delicious dinner for this meat-eating Dilophosaurus.

DINO REPORT

NAME: Dilophosaurus
(die-LOAF-oh-sore-us)

MEANING:
Two-ridged lizard

SIZE:

FOOD: Meat

Two bony crests.

Sharp, curved teeth.

Short arms.

DID YOU KNOW?

Dilophosaurus had a jaw similar to a crocodile's.

Long back legs for running fast.

T. rex Teasers

Use the key to work out the answers to these questions about the fearsome Tyrannosaurus.

KEY

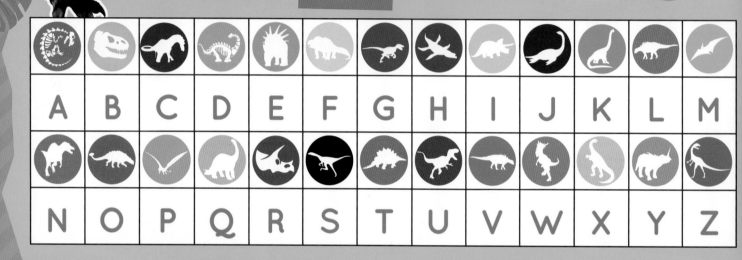

1 What did Tyrannosaurus have that was twice as big as those of other giant carnivores?

___ ___ ___ ___ ___

2 Which part of Tyrannosaurus's body was small compared to the rest?

___ ___ ___ ___

3 What did Tyrannosaurus have 50-60 of?

___ ___ ___ ___ ___

Answers on pages 76-77.

Footprint Fun

Look out, there are dinosaurs about! Can you match these dino footprints into pairs?

Can you stomp like a dinosaur?

Colour the dinosaur when you've finished.

Answers on pages 76-77.

67

Hefty Ankylosaurus

This bulky dino was as large as a tank.

Tough armour made it hard to attack.

Tail club for attacking.

WOW!

Ankylosaurus lived in Canada and the USA 74-67 million years ago.

DINO REPORT

NAME: Ankylosaurus
(an-KIE-loh-sore-us)

MEANING: Stiff lizard

SIZE:

FOOD: Plants

Walked on four legs.

DID YOU KNOW?

Ankylosaurus didn't chew its food, instead it was broken down inside its powerful stomach.

68

Join the dots to finish this Ankylosaurus picture, then colour it in.

DINO DOT-TO-DOT

Small teeth behind a horny beak.

DID YOU KNOW?

Ankylosaurus was wider than it was tall.

Design a Dino

Use this space to create your very own, one-of-a-kind dinosaur.

MY DINO REPORT

My dinosaur is called

It is the size of a

It likes to eat

It weighs as much as

My dinosaur is FRIENDLY ☐   FIERCE ☐

WILL YOUR DINOSAUR BE...?

Draw your dino here.

Spotty?

Stripy?

How long is your dinosaur's tail?

Does your dinosaur have lots of teeth?

Dinosaur Imposters!

These pre-historic reptiles are often mistaken for dinosaurs.

PTERANODON
(te-RAN-o-don)

Huge wings.

Tall crest.

Toothless beak.

FLYING FUN

Look carefully at the flying Pteranodons. Can you spot the odd one out?

A

B

C

Answers on pages 76-77.

72

DIMETRODON
(die-MEE-tro-don)

DID YOU KNOW?
The Dimetrodon lived before the dinosaurs, about 275 million years ago.

Large sail.

Lots of different kinds of teeth.

Walked on four legs.

DID YOU KNOW?
The Dimetrodon had hidden teeth on the roof of its mouth to keep hold of struggling prey.

SHADOW MATCH

Which shadow matches this Dimetrodon picture exactly?

Answers on pages 76-77.

A   B   C

73

DID YOU KNOW?

Kronosaurus lived in the Australian seas around 100 million years ago.

Four flippers.

Pointed teeth.

DID YOU KNOW?

The ginormous Kronosaurus was as long as a bus.

Long body.

HOW BIG?

Colour the bus to show how long a Kronosaurus was.

PLESIOSAURUS
(PLE-see-oh-SORE-us)

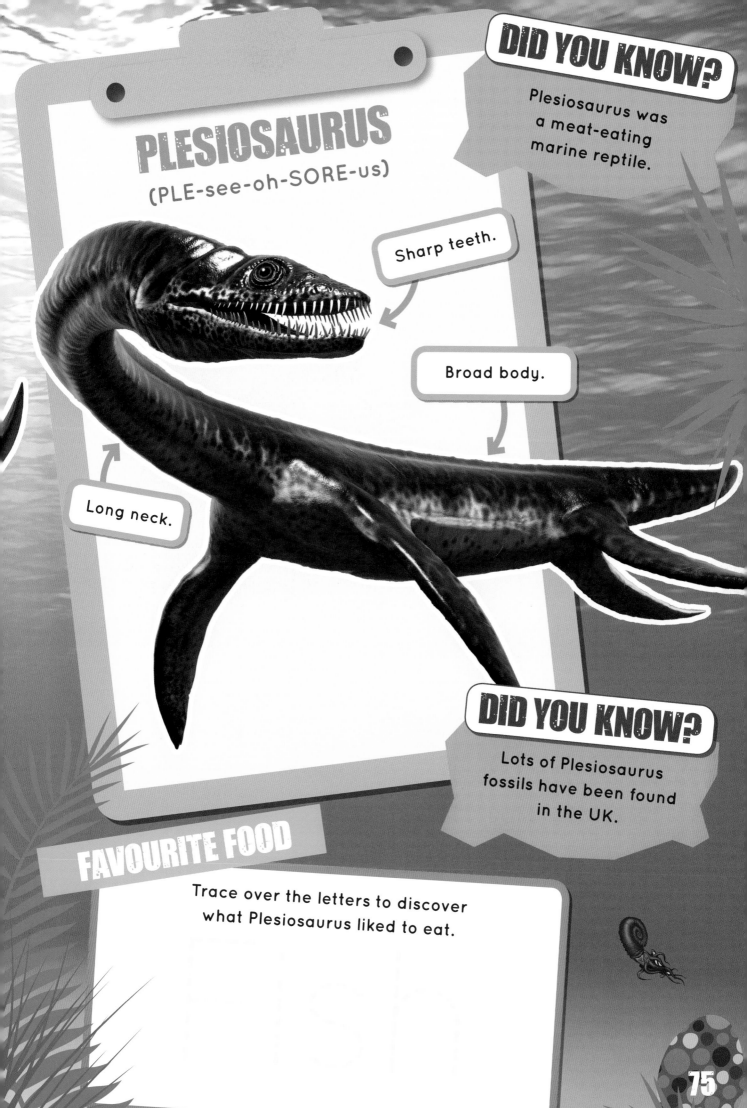

DID YOU KNOW?

Plesiosaurus was a meat-eating marine reptile.

Sharp teeth.

Broad body.

Long neck.

DID YOU KNOW?

Lots of Plesiosaurus fossils have been found in the UK.

FAVOURITE FOOD

Trace over the letters to discover what Plesiosaurus liked to eat.

75

Answers

p 6-7
A belongs to Tyrannosaurus.

p 8-9

2 3 1 4 5

p 10-11
There are 15 leaves.

p 14-15
There are 7 eggs.

p 18-19
B is the odd one out.

p 22-23

p 24-25
A is the biggest.

p 26-27
There are 6 baby dinos.

p 28-29

p 30-31
1 = C, 2 = D, 3 = A, 4 = B.

p 34-35

F	O	O	T	P	R	I	N	T	A	P
Y	S	T	E	O	T	F	I	J	O	R
A	F	R	T	H	O	R	N	T	U	E
K	O	L	S	A	R	E	D	E	I	H
M	S	F	Z	N	O	K	E	G	S	I
C	S	F	S	E	Y	W	V	G	I	S
T	I	U	I	S	K	G	G	D	S	T
N	L	C	A	T	A	O	J	E	S	O
B	G	R	P	R	E	D	A	T	O	R
S	A	C	E	V	X	S	P	R	J	I
B	O	N	E	S	D	O	V	H	H	C

p 36-37
C doesn't belong to Giganotosaurus.

p 42-43

76

p 44-45

p 48-49
C is the smallest Microraptor.

p 52-53
Path B will take Allosaurus home.

p 60-61

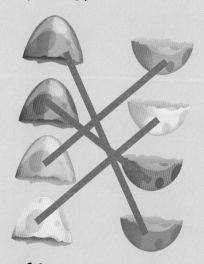

p 66

1.

B R A I N
_ _ _ _ _

2.

A R M S
_ _ _ _

3.

T E E T H
_ _ _ _ _

p 67
1 = 6, 2 = 8, 3 = 7, 4 = 5.

p 72
B is the odd one out.

p 73
A matches the picture exactly.